Our Story
for my son

Our Story
- for my son

Our Story will inspire you to capture the unique story of you and your son. Allow an enjoyable hour or two once a year to complete your journal – a great opportunity to reflect on your remarkable relationship.

Our Story helps you to record your amazing family experiences and unrepeatable moments – the growth, development and personality of your son, your time together and your emotional journey – your hopes and dreams, the ups and downs and above all, the incredible son bond.

On your son's 18th birthday he can receive this beautiful handwritten story, a priceless record of your years together, to be shared and treasured forever.

Our Story for

ME

Date of birth …

Place of birth …

Eye color …

Hair color …

Blood group …

My mother's name …

My father's name …

Education …

Jobs …

You

Date of birth …

Time of birth …

Place of birth …

Who was there …

Birth weight …

Hair color …

Blood group …

Mother's name …

Father's name …

Who you look like …

"There are two lasting bequests we can
hope to give our children.
One of those is roots, the other is wings."

Hodding Carter

Our
First
Year
Together

Date

A few of your favorite things . . .

A few of my favorite things . . .

FOR THE RECORD

Where we live . . .

Who we live with . . .

Shipment ID: ZL4E61BD1C
Shipping Facility: C   Ship Date: Feb 23, 2019

If you ordered multiple items, we may send you separate packages so that you receive them faster.

SHIP TO

SANDRA O'TOOLE

QTY	PRODUCT DESCRIPTION
1	'Our Story for My Son' Memory Book - One-Size SKU: 24667101

We want you to love your finds!

In case something is not as expected, check its return eligibility by visiting zulily.com/account/orders (US customers only) or emailing service@zulily.com

133100967

1

How I feel about our year together . . .

Ailments this year . . .

1

What you are like …

1

Things you have done and said …

Things that have happened in the world this year…

1

Adventures we have had this year...

Adventures I would love to have with you in the coming year...

My hopes and dreams for the next 12 months . . .

My predictions of what you will be like when you grow up . . .

"A mother's arms are more comforting than anyone else's."

Diana, Princess of Wales

Our
Second
Year
Together

Date

2

A few of your favorite things . . .

A few of my favorite things . . .

FOR THE RECORD

Where we live . . .

Who we live with . . .

2

How I feel about our year together …

2

What you are like . . .

Things you have done and said . . .

2

Things that have happened in the world this year...

Adventures we have had this year...

Adventures I would love to have with you in the coming year...

My hopes and dreams for the next 12 months...

My predictions of what you will be like when you grow up...

"When you are a mother, you are never really alone in your thoughts. A mother always has to think twice, once for herself and once for her child."

Sophia Loren

Our

Year Together

Date

3

A few of your favorite things ...

A few of my favorite things ...

FOR THE RECORD

Where we live ...

Who we live with ...

3

How I feel about our year together . . .

3

What you are like ...

Things you have done and said...

Things that have happened in the world this year...

3

Adventures we have had this year...

Adventures I would love to have with you in the coming year...

My hopes and dreams for the next 12 months…

My predictions of what you will be like when you grow up…

"Parenting is a stage in life's journey where the milestones come about every fifty feet."

Robert Brault

Our Fourth Year Together

Date

4

A few of your favorite things . . .

A few of my favorite things . . .

FOR THE RECORD

Where we live . . .

Who we live with . . .

4

How I feel about our year together . . .

What you are like . . .

Things you have done and said . . .

4

Things that have happened in the world this year...

Adventures we have had this year...

Adventures I would love to have with you in the coming year...

My hopes and dreams for the next 12 months ...

My predictions of what you will be like when you grow up ...

"Family life is a bit like a runny apple pie - not perfect but who's complaining."

Author Unknown

Our Fifth Year Together

Date

5

A few of your favorite things ...

A few of my favorite things ...

FOR THE RECORD

Where we live ...

Who we live with ...

5

How I feel about our year together . . .

Ailments this year . . .

5

What you are like…

Things you have done and said ...

Things that have happened in the world this year...

Adventures we have had this year...

Adventures I would love to have with you in the coming year...

My hopes and dreams for the next 12 months…

My predictions of what you will be like when you grow up…

"Instant availability without continuous presence is probably the best role a mother can play."

Lotte Baily

Our Sixth Year Together

Date

6

A few of your favorite things . . .

A few of my favorite things . . .

FOR THE RECORD

Where we live . . .

Who we live with . . .

6

How I feel about our year together …

What you are like …

Things you have done and said …

6

Things that have happened in the world this year…

Adventures we have had this year...

Adventures I would love to have with you in the coming year...

My hopes and dreams for the next 12 months . . .

My predictions of what you will be like when you grow up . . .

A boy's best friend is his mother."

Joseph Stephano

Our
Seventh
Year
Together

Date

7

A few of your favorite things . . .

A few of my favorite things . . .

FOR THE RECORD

Where we live . . .

Who we live with . . .

7

How I feel about our year together …

Ailments this year …

What you are like…

Things you have done and said . . .

Things that have happened in the world this year . . .

7

Adventures we have had this year…

Adventures I would love to have with you in the coming year…

My hopes and dreams for the next 12 months …

My predictions of what you will be like when you grow up …

"If you want a baby, have a new one. Don't baby the old one."

Jessamyn West

Our
Eighth
Year Together

Date

8

A few of your favorite things ...

A few of my favorite things ...

FOR THE RECORD

Where we live ...

Who we live with ...

8

How I feel about our year together . . .

Ailments this year . . .

What you are like . . .

Things you have done and said . . .

8

Things that have happened in the world this year…

Adventures we have had this year…

Adventures I would love to have with you in the coming year…

My hopes and dreams for the next 12 months …

My predictions of what you will be like when you grow up …

"A child seldom needs a good talking to as a good listening to."

Angela Schwindt

Our Ninth Year Together

Date

9

A few of your favorite things . . .

A few of my favorite things . . .

FOR THE RECORD

Where we live . . .

Who we live with . . .

9

How I feel about our year together ...

Ailments this year ...

What you are like . . .

Things you have done and said…

Things that have happened in the world this year…

Adventures we have had this year...

Adventures I would love to have with you in the coming year...

My hopes and dreams for the next 12 months …

My predictions of what you will be like when you grow up …

"A child's greatest period of growth is the month after you have purchased new school shoes."

Author Unknown

Our
Tenth
Year Together

Date

10

A few of your favorite things ...

A few of my favorite things ...

FOR THE RECORD

Where we live ...

Who we live with ...

10

How I feel about our year together . . .

Ailments this year . . .

What you are like . . .

Things you have done and said . . .

10

Things that have happened in the world this year . . .

Adventures we have had this year...

Adventures I would love to have with you in the coming year...

My hopes and dreams for the next 12 months …

My predictions of what you will be like when you grow up …

"There are three ways to get things done: do it yourself, employ someone or forbid your children to do it."

Monta Crane

Our
Eleventh
Year
Together

Date

A few of your favorite things . . .

A few of my favorite things . . .

FOR THE RECORD

Where we live . . .

Who we live with . . .

How I feel about our year together . . .

Ailments this year . . .

What you are like . . .

Things you have done and said…

Things that have happened in the world this year…

Adventures we have had this year...

Adventures I would love to have with you in the coming year...

My hopes and dreams for the next 12 months . . .

My predictions of what you will be like when you grow up . . .

"One thing a mother must always save for a rainy day is patience."

Author Unknown

Our
Twelfth
Year
Together

Date

A few of your favorite things . . .

A few of my favorite things . . .

FOR THE RECORD

Where we live . . .

Who we live with . . .

12

How I feel about our year together ...

What you are like . . .

Things you have done and said . . .

12

Things that have happened in the world this year . . .

Adventures we have had this year...

Adventures I would love to have with you in the coming year...

My hopes and dreams for the next 12 months . . .

My predictions of what you will be like when you grow up . . .

"It is the little things in common that make relationships enjoyable . . . but it is the little differences that make them interesting."

Todd Ruthman

Our Thirteenth Year Together

Date

A few of your favorite things ...

A few of my favorite things ...

FOR THE RECORD

Where we live ...

Who we live with ...

How I feel about our year together . . .

13

What you are like . . .

Things you have done and said…

Things that have happened in the world this year…

Adventures we have had this year…

Adventures I would love to have with you in the coming year…

My hopes and dreams for the next 12 months …

My predictions of what you will be like when you grow up …

"Where parents do too much for their children, the children will not do much for themselves."

Elbert Hubbard

Our Fourteenth Year Together

Date

14

A few of your favorite things . . .

A few of my favorite things . . .

FOR THE RECORD

Where we live . . .

Who we live with . . .

14

How I feel about our year together . . .

Ailments this year . . .

What you are like . . .

Things you have done and said . . .

14

Things that have happened in the world this year...

Adventures we have had this year...

Adventures I would love to have with you in the coming year...

14

My hopes and dreams for the next 12 months …

My predictions of what you will be like when you grow up …

"At fourteen you don't need sickness or death for tragedy."

Jessamyn West

Our
Fifteenth
Year Together

Date

15

A few of your favorite things . . .

A few of my favorite things . . .

FOR THE RECORD

Where we live . . .

Who we live with . . .

How I feel about our year together …

What you are like . . .

Things you have done and said . . .

Things that have happened in the world this year . . .

15

Adventures we have had this year...

Adventures I would love to have with you in the coming year...

My hopes and dreams for the next 12 months...

My predictions of what you will be like when you grow up...

"Being a mother means your heart is no longer yours, it wanders wherever your children do."

Author Unknown

Our
Sixteenth
Year
Together

Date

A few of your favorite things . . .

A few of my favorite things . . .

FOR THE RECORD

Where we live . . .

Who we live with . . .

16

How I feel about our year together …

Ailments this year …

What you are like...

Things you have done and said...

16

Things that have happened in the world this year...

Adventures we have had this year...

Adventures I would love to have with you in the coming year...

My hopes and dreams for the next 12 months…

My predictions of what you will be like when you grow up…

"To an adolescent, there is nothing in the world more embarrassing than a parent."

Dave Barry

Our
Our Seventeenth
Year
Together

Date

17

A few of your favorite things . . .

A few of my favorite things . . .

FOR THE RECORD

Where we live . . .

Who we live with . . .

How I feel about our year together . . .

What you are like . . .

Things you have done and said . . .

Things that have happened in the world this year . . .

Adventures we have had this year…

Adventures I would love to have with you in the coming year…

My hopes and dreams for the next 12 months ...

My predictions of what you will be like when you grow up ...

"Adolescence is perhaps Nature's way of preparing parents to welcome the empty nest."

Karen Savage and Patricia Adams

Our Eighteenth Year Together

Date

A few of your favorite things ...

A few of my favorite things ...

FOR THE RECORD

Where we live ...

Who we live with ...

18

How I feel about our year together . . .

Ailments this year . . .

What you are like . . .

Things you have done and said . . .

18

Things that have happened in the world this year...

Adventures we have had this year...

Adventures I would love to have with you in the coming year...

My hopes and dreams for our futures are . . .

"When you have brought up kids,
there are memories you store
directly in your tear ducts."

Robert Brault

What I love about you…

My words of advice for the next stage of your life are . . .

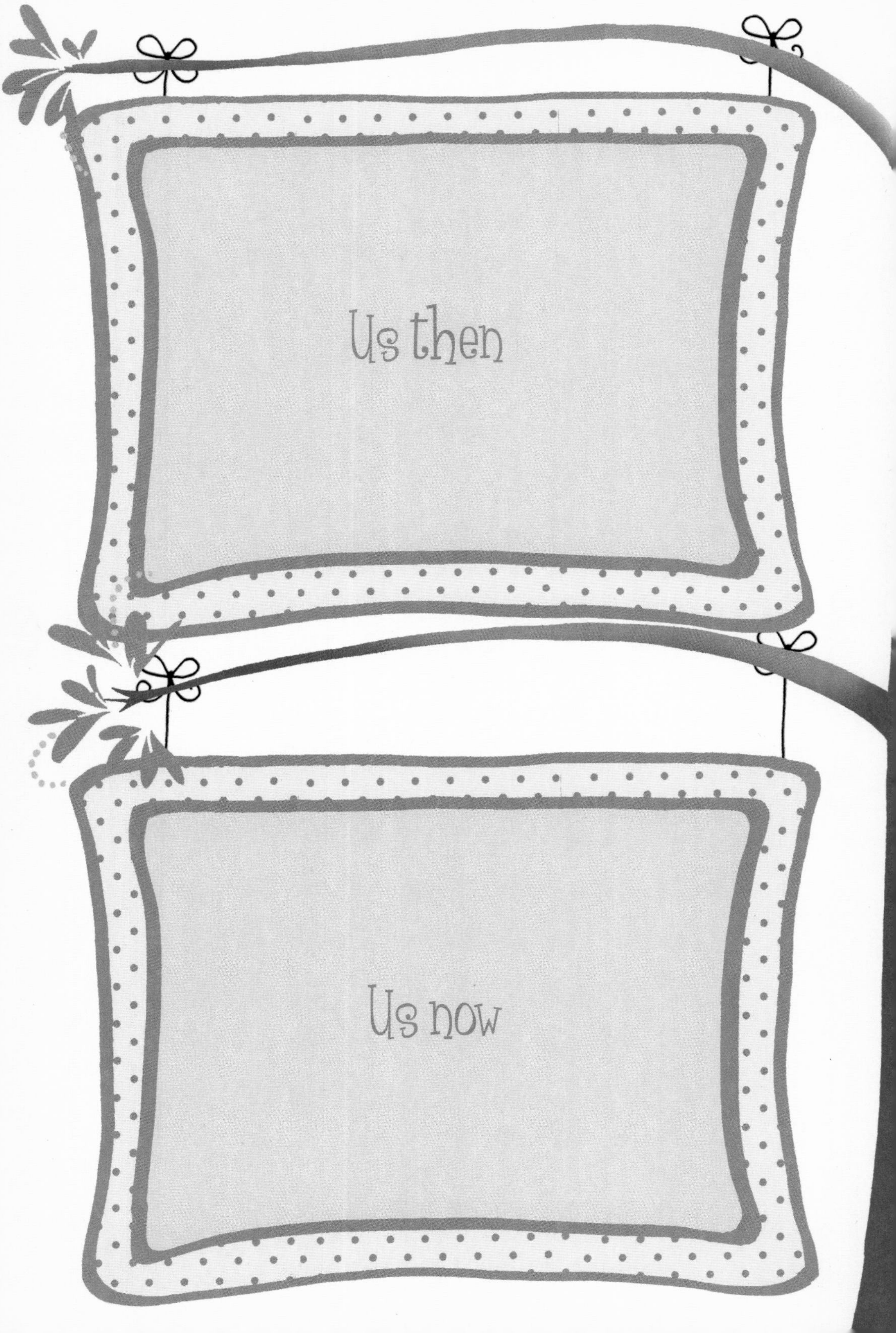
Us then
Us now

"Home is where we tie one
end of the thread of life."

Martin Buxbaum

Our Story – for my son

First published (US version) by *from you to me* limited, April 2013

ISBN 978–1–907048–50–0

Every effort has been made to credit all quoted material correctly; should there by any errors or omissions in this respect we apologise and shall be pleased to make the appropriate changes in any future edition.

Designed by Helen Stephens and Lucy Tapper.

Printed and bound in China by Imago.

This paper is manufactured from pulp sourced from forests that are legally and sustainably managed.

For more information please contact:
from you to me ltd
The Cottage Suite, The Old Brewery, Wine Street,
Bradford on Avon, BA15 1NS, England, UK.

Email: mail@fromyoutome.com

For tips, information and help on completing your journal please go to
www.fromyoutome.com/share

Published by from you to me ltd

from you to me Journals of a Lifetime*

Dear Mom
Dear Dad
Dear Grandma
Dear Grandpa
Dear Daughter
Dear Son
Dear Sister
Dear Brother
Dear Friend

*Also available to personalize online at www.fromyoutome.us

Home & Garden Journals

Cooking up Memories

Parent & Child

Bump to Birthday – pregnancy & first year journal
Our Story – for my daughter
Our Story – for my son

Christmas Memories

Christmas Present, Christmas Past

Anniversary & Relationship

Love Stories

All titles are available at gift and book shops or www.fromyoutome.us

Follow us on Facebook and Twitter and read our blogs at
http://fromyoutomeltd.blogspot.co.uk

for each and every child

www.fromyoutome.us